DILBERT™

Book of Days

For a free catalog of other Cedco® products, please write to the address above, or visit our website: www.cedco.com

ISBN 0-7683-2030-5

Published 1998

1 3 5 7 9 10 8 6 4 2

January 1	January 2	January 3

January 4

January 5

Pop.
9:15 - City Hall

January 6

January 7

DOGBERT, I NEED YOU TO FACILITATE SOME MEETINGS.

WHAT KIND OF MEETINGS?

WE'RE CREATING A PROCESS TO FIX OUR PRODUCT DEVELOPMENT PROCESS. BUT FIRST WE'RE HAVING SOME PREPLANNING MEETINGS...

...TO DECIDE ON A PROJECT NAME.

HOW ABOUT "DEATH SPIRAL"?

January 8

January 9

January 10

January 11

January 12

January 13

WOULDN'T IT BE FUNNY IF WE WERE ALL LITTLE DOGS!

HIT ME.

S. Adams

Another reason you shouldn't invite your boss to play cards

January 14	January 15	January 16

Nata

Diagnostic - Wedsonday

Jan 14th - 12:30

January 17

January 18

January 19

WE'LL SUCCEED IF WE UNDERSTAND WHO OUR COMPETITORS REALLY ARE!

MY COMPETITION IS DILBERT AND ALICE, WITH WHOM I COMPETE FOR SALARY INCREASES AND RARE PROMOTION OPPORTUNITIES.

I MEANT OUR EXTERNAL COMPETI-TION.

TELL ME AGAIN WHAT WE MAKE.

NO RAISE FOR YOU, IDIOT BOY.

January 20	January 21	January 22

January 23

January 24

January 25

January 26

January 27

January 28

January 29

January 30

January 31

February 1

_____
_____
_____
_____
_____
_____
_____
_____

February 2

_____
_____
_____
_____
_____
_____
_____
_____

February 3	February 4	February 5

February 6

February 7

February 8

February 9

February 10

February 11

THE BUSINESS PLAN FOR YOUR START-UP IS IDIOTIC BUT I'M GOING TO PROVIDE THE VENTURE CAPITAL FUNDING ANYWAY.

WE'LL GENERATE LOTS OF MEDIA HYPE, GO PUBLIC AND MAKE MILLIONS BY SHAFTING GREEDY AND IGNORANT INVESTORS.

THE LATIN WORD FOR "CLOSE YOUR EYES AND OPEN YOUR MOUTH" IS "PROSPECTUS."

THIS IS EXACTLY WHY I'M AFRAID OF DOGS.

S. Adams   E-mail: SCOTTADAMS@AOL.COM   © 1998 United Feature Syndicate, Inc. (NYC)

February 15

February 16

February 17

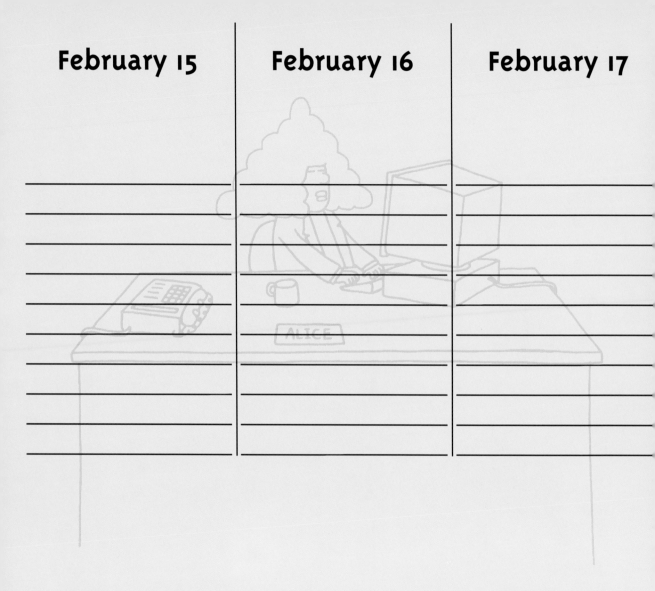

February 18	February 19	February 20

February 21

February 22

February 23

February 24	February 25	February 26

February 27 | February 28 | February 29

March 1	March 2

March 3

March 4

March 5

HERE'S YOUR PROBLEM. THE CONNECTION TO THE NETWORK IS BROKEN.

UH-OH. IT'S A "TOKEN RING" LAN. THAT MEANS THE TOKEN FELL OUT AND IT'S IN THIS ROOM SOMEPLACE

YOU ARE THE WIND BENEATH MY WINGS

I'LL WAIT A WEEK THEN TELL HIM THE TOKEN MUST BE IN THE "ETHERNET."

S. Adams   E-mail: SCOTTADAMS@AOL.COM

5/1/96 © 1996 United Feature Syndicate, Inc.(NYC)

March 6	March 7	March 8

March 9 **March 10** **March 11**

March 12

March 13

March 14

March 15

March 16

March 17

March 18	March 19	March 20
_____	_____	_____
_____	_____	_____
_____	_____	_____
_____	_____	_____
_____	_____	_____
_____	_____	_____
_____	_____	_____
_____	_____	_____

March 21

March 22

March 23

Focazio visit

March 24

March 25

March 26

March 27	March 28	March 29
		office visit aversa

Panel 1: CAROL, THE NEXT TIME YOU ORDER MY BUSINESS CARDS, SPELL OUT MY FULL TITLE: "DIRECTOR OF PRODUCT ENHANCEMENTS."

Panel 2: DON'T USE THE ACRONYM "DOPE."

Panel 3: I DIDN'T KNOW YOU WERE THE DIRECTOR OF PRODUCT ENHANCEMENTS.

S. Adams E-mail: SCOTTADAMS@AOL.COM

© 1995 United Feature Syndicate, Inc. (NYC)

March 30	March 31	April 1

April 2

April 3

April 4

April 5

go for
glasses

hrs. 1-7 afternoon

April 6

? allergy

April 7

April 8

Call Zalkowitz
growth in fluid

April 9

NOBODY HAS TEN YEARS EXPERIENCE WITH NEW TECH-NOLOGY! YOU'RE JUST BEING EVIL. ADMIT IT.

AND COULD YOU PLEASE SHAKE YOUR HEAD BACK AND FORTH INSTEAD OF SPINNING IT AROUND?

April 10

April 11

April 12

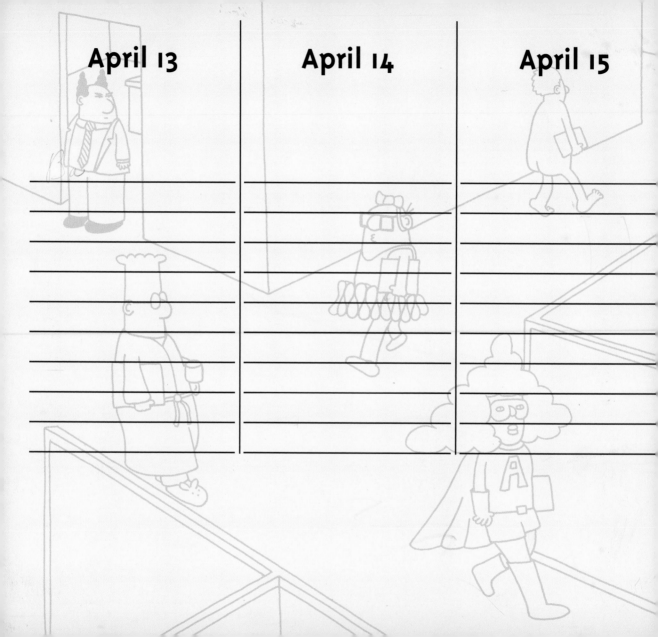

April 13

April 14

April 15

April 16	April 17	April 18
1-770-804-9250		Lawyer ASAP
Christopher Bertoni		Brian Tracey
4906 SPRING CREEK LANE		Rutherford
ATLANTA, GA 30350		

April 19

Monday
call Express
Script for
Frank

April 20

April 21

THE COMPANY ANNOUNCED THAT WE WILL "ABANDON OUR STRATEGY OF MAKING GOOD PRODUCTS..."

FROM NOW ON WE'LL "PURSUE A DESPERATE STRATEGY OF MERGERS, BUSINESS SPIN-OFFS, FRUITLESS PARTNERSHIPS AND RANDOM REORGANIZATIONS."

"AND WE'LL ACCELERATE OUR PROGRAM OF PAYING THE GOOD EMPLOYEES TO LEAVE."

STOCK PRICE?

UP THREE POINTS.

www.unitedmedia.com

S. Adams

9/13/96 © 1996 United Feature Syndicate, Inc. (NYC)

April 22

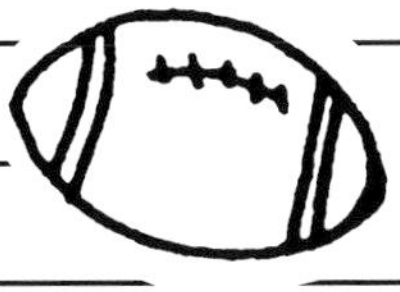

April 23

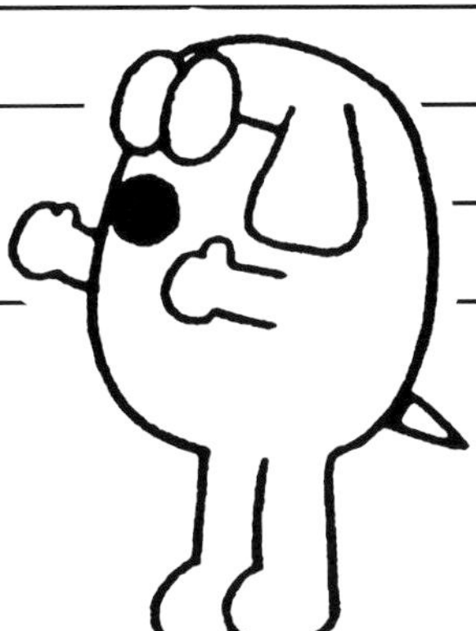

April 24

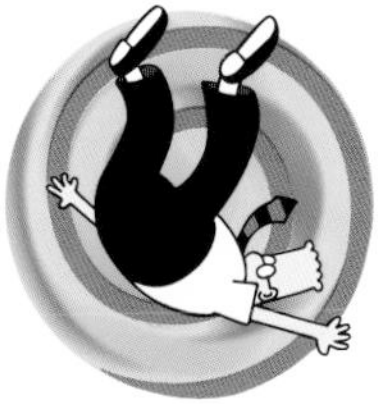

April 25

April 26

April 27

April 28

April 29

April 30

May 1

May 2

May 3

May 4

May 5

May 6

May 7

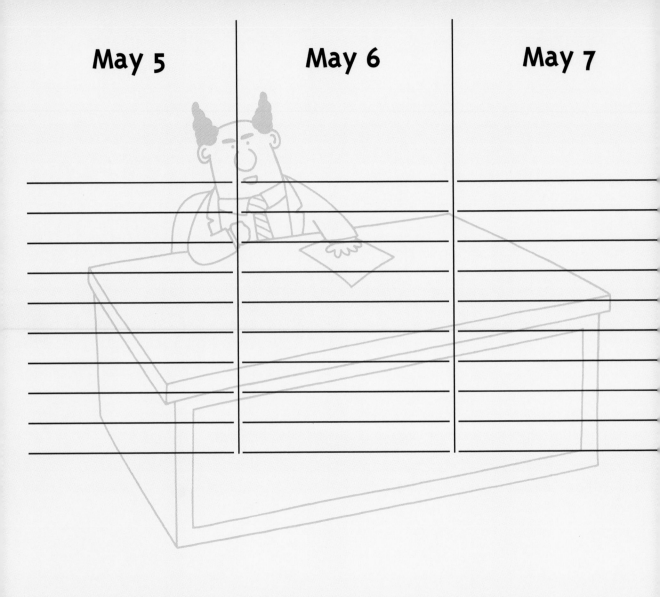

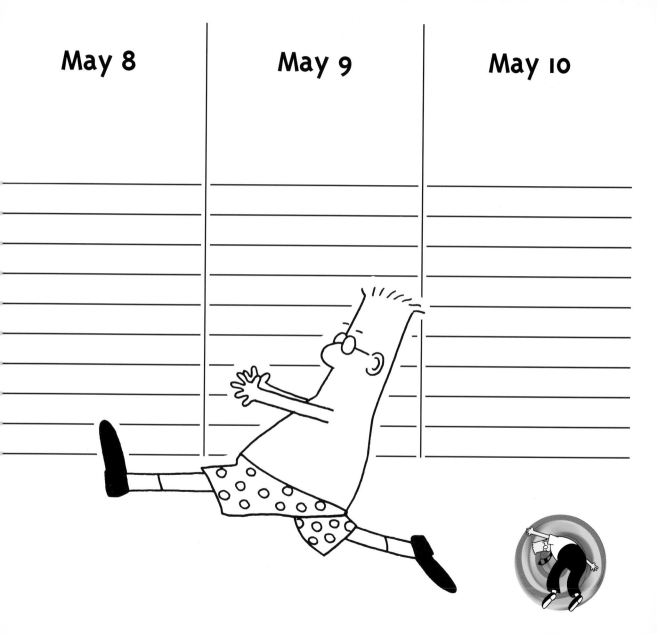

May 11

May 12

Blood work

May 13

Battles
Blood work

May 14	May 15	May 16

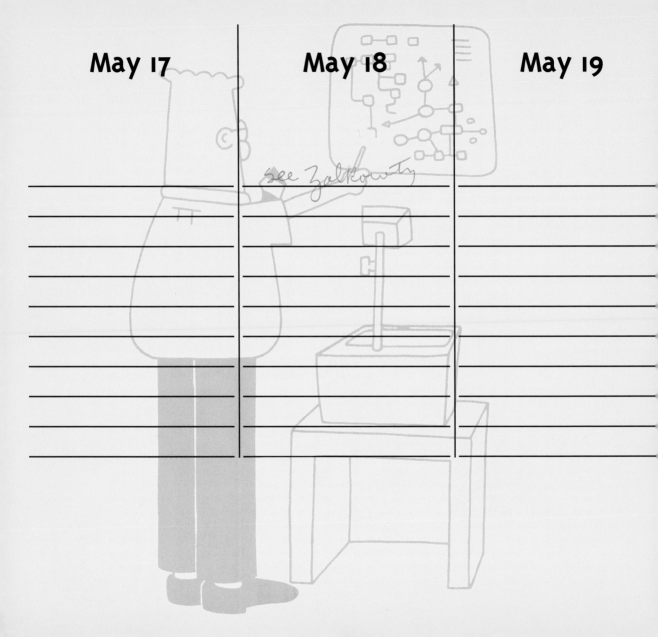

May 20	May 21	May 22

May 23

May 24

May 25

May 26	May 27	May 28
_____	_____	_____
_____	_____	_____
_____	_____	_____
_____	_____	_____
_____	_____	_____
_____	_____	_____
_____	_____	_____
_____	_____	_____
_____	_____	_____
_____		

May 29	May 30	May 31

June 1

_____
_____
_____
_____
_____
_____
_____
_____
_____

June 2

_____
_____
_____
_____
_____
_____
_____
_____
_____

June 3

June 4

June 5

June 6

June 7

June 8

June 9	June 10	June 11

June 12

June 13

June 14

June 15

June 16

June 17

June 18	June 19	June 20

June 21	June 22	June 23

June 24	June 25	June 26
_____	_____	_____
_____	_____	_____
_____	_____	_____
_____	_____	_____
_____	_____	_____
_____	_____	_____
_____	_____	_____
_____	_____	_____
_____	_____	_____
_____	_____	_____

June 27	June 28	June 29
_____	_____	_____
_____	_____	_____
_____	_____	_____
_____	_____	_____
_____	_____	_____
_____	_____	_____
_____	_____	_____
_____	_____	_____
_____	_____	_____

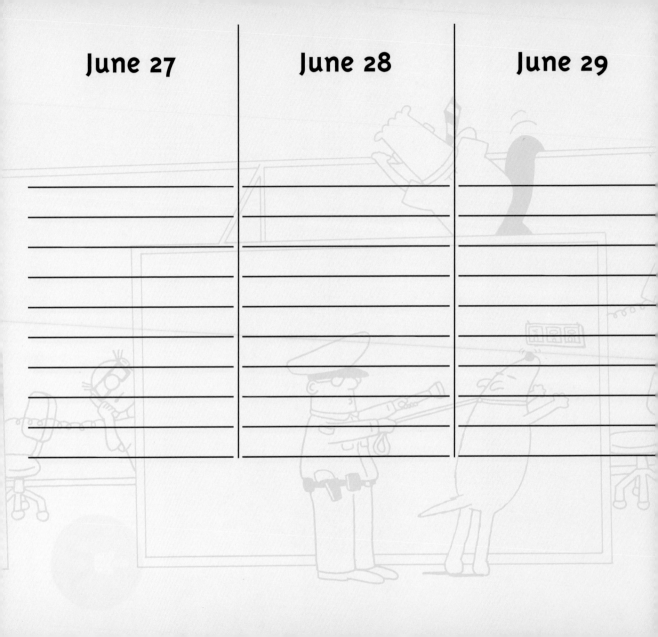

June 30

July 1

July 2

July 3

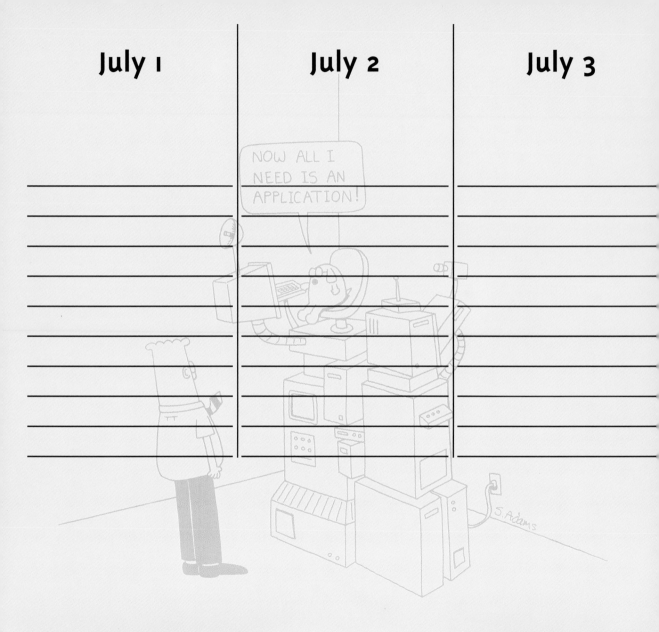

July 4

July 5

July 6

July 7	July 8	July 9

OUT OUT!!
YOU DEMONS OF
STUPIDITY!!

July 10	July 11	July 12

July 13

July 14

July 15

July 16	July 17	July 18

July 19

July 20

July 21

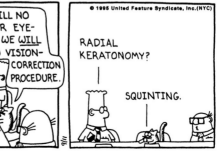

AS DIRECTOR OF HUMAN RESOURCES I'VE BEEN ASKED TO REDUCE THE COST OF EMPLOYEE BENEFITS.

THE COMPANY WILL NO LONGER PAY FOR EYE-GLASSES. BUT WE WILL SUPPORT A NEW VISION-CORRECTION PROCEDURE.

RADIAL KERATONOMY?

SQUINTING.

July 22	July 23	July 24

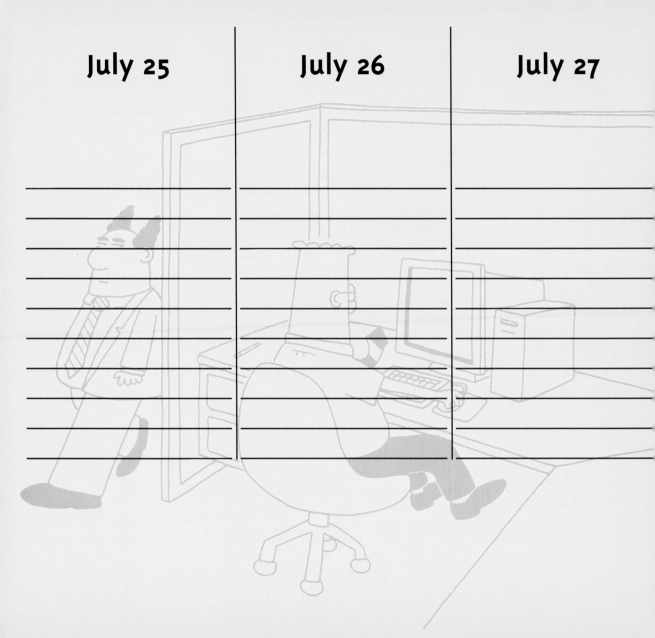

July 25

July 26

July 27

July 28

July 29

July 30

July 31

August 1

August 2

I DON'T UNDERSTAND HOW THE NEW REORGAN-IZATION WILL HELP US "FOCUS ON OUR CORE BUSINESS."

DID OUR CORE BUSINESS CHANGE? OR ARE YOU SAYING THAT EVERY REORG PRIOR TO THIS WAS A MISDIRECTED FAILURE?

WALLY, WHEN A CAR GETS A FLAT TIRE, WHAT DO YOU DO?

WELL, IF I'M YOU, I ROTATE THE TIRES AND DRIVE HOME.

E-mail: SCOTTADAMS@AOL.COM

© 1995 United Feature Syndicate, Inc.(NYC)

August 3

_____
_____
_____
_____
_____
_____
_____
_____
_____
_____

August 4

_____
_____
_____
_____
_____
_____
_____
_____
_____

August 5

August 6

August 7

August 8	August 9	August 10

August 11

August 12

August 13

August 14	August 15	August 16

August 17

August 18

August 19

August 20

August 21

August 22

August 23	August 24	August 25

August 26

August 27

August 28

August 29	August 30	August 31

September 1

September 2

September 3

September 4

September 5	September 6	September 7

September 8	September 9	September 10

September 11

September 12

September 13

September 14

September 15

September 16

September 17

_____
_____
_____
_____
_____
_____
_____
_____
_____
_____

September 18

_____
_____
_____
_____
_____
_____
_____
_____
_____

September 19

_____
_____
_____
_____
_____
_____
_____
_____
_____

September 20	September 21	September 22

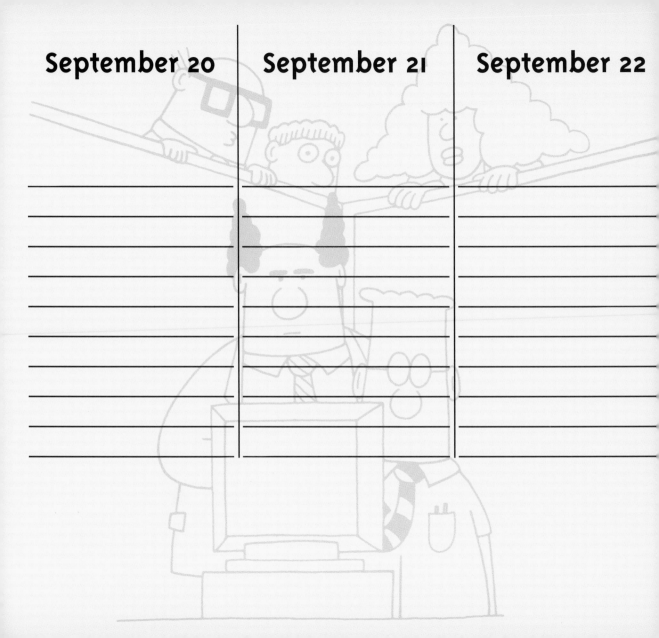

September 23

September 24

September 25

September 26

September 27

September 28

September 29

September 30

October 1	October 2	October 3

October 4	October 5	October 6

October 7

October 8

October 9

CATBERT THE HR DIRECTOR

HERE'S THE NEW ORG CHART. MAYBE YOU'RE ON IT AND MAYBE NOT.

OOH! NICE TRY! SO CLOSE. TOO BAD.

IT'S FUN TO PLAY WITH THEM BEFORE DOWNSIZING THEM.

S. Adams

E-mail: SCOTTADAMS@AOL.COM

© 1995 United Feature Syndicate, Inc. (NYC)

October 10

_____
_____
_____
_____
_____
_____
_____
_____
_____
_____

October 11

_____
_____
_____
_____
_____
_____
_____
_____
_____
_____

October 12

_____
_____
_____
_____
_____
_____
_____
_____
_____
_____

October 13

October 14

October 15

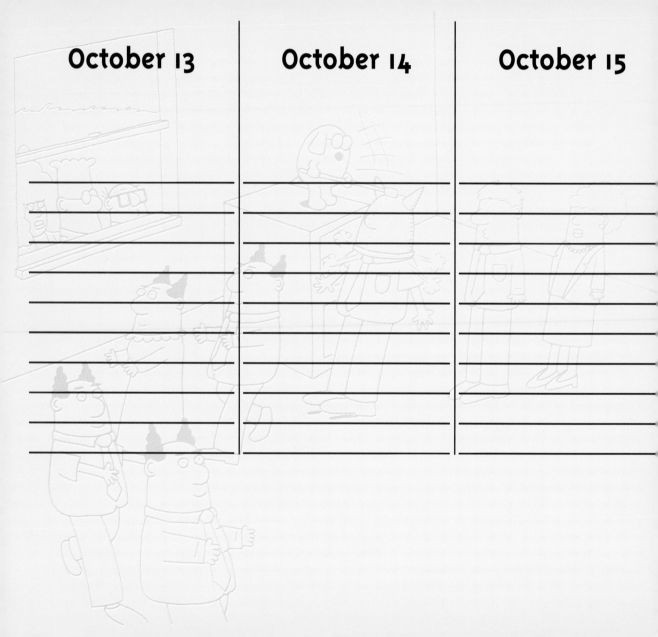

October 16

October 17

October 18

October 19

October 20

October 21

October 22	October 23	October 24

October 25

October 26

October 27

October 30

October 31

November 1

MANAGER TRAINING

NEVER BE IN THE SAME ROOM AS A DECISION.

DECISION

YOU

I'LL ILLUSTRATE MY POINT WITH A PUPPET SHOW THAT I CALL...

"JOURNEY TO BLAMEVILLE," STARRING "SUGGESTION SAM" AND "MANAGER MEG."

November 2	November 3	November 4

November 5	November 6	November 7

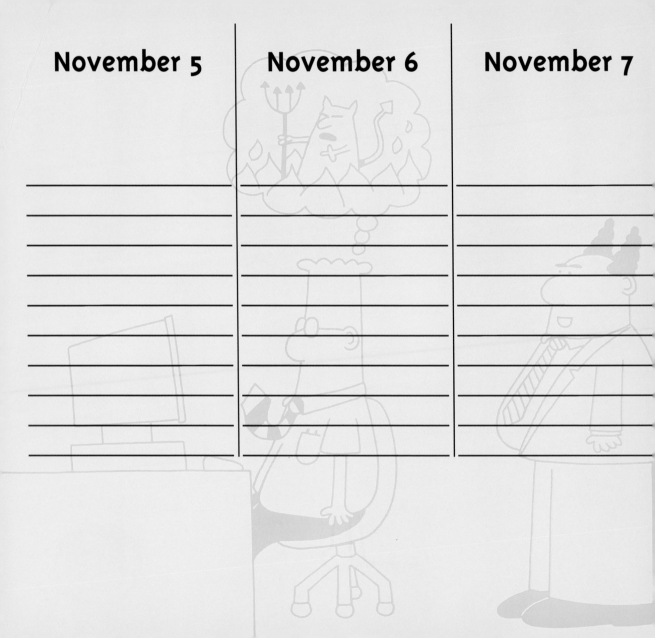

November 8	November 9	November 10

November 11

November 12

November 13

RATBERT THE TEMP WORKER

THIS IS REALLY TESTING MY SENSE OF SELF-WORTH.

I WILL COMPENSATE BY SHOUTING A LIST OF MY TALENTS TO ANYBODY WHO WALKS PAST.

IGNORE HIM. HE'S TRYING TO TRICK US INTO MAKING EYE CONTACT.

I EAT RUBBER! I CARRY DISEASE! I ENJOY OPERA!

November 14	November 15	November 16
_____	_____	_____

November 17	November 18	November 19

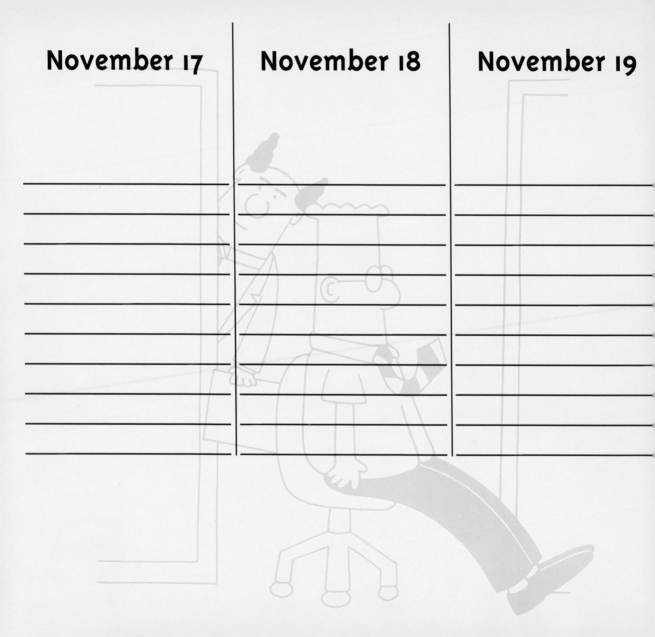

November 20	November 21	November 22

November 23

November 24

November 25

MISTER CATBERT, THE COMPANY IS TRYING TO FORCE ME TO USE A DIFFERENT KIND OF COMPUTER.

YOU'RE THE HUMAN RESOURCES DIRECTOR. WHAT ARE YOU DOING TO STOP THIS RELIGIOUS PERSECUTION??! WHAT EVER HAPPENED TO "DIVERSITY"??

THE LONGER YOU VERK HERE, DIVERSE IT GETS.

NEXT.

S.ADAMS E-mail: SCOTTADAMS@AOL.COM

© 1995 United Feature Syndicate, Inc. (NYC)

November 26	November 27	November 28

November 29	November 30	December 1

December 2

December 3

December 4

December 5

December 6

December 7

December 8

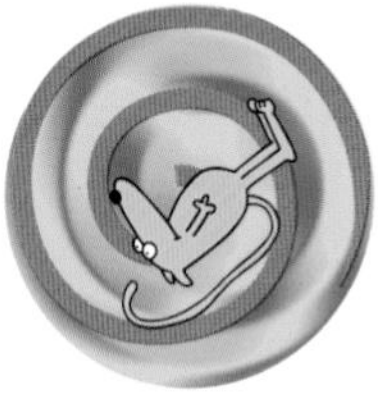

December 9

December 10

December 11

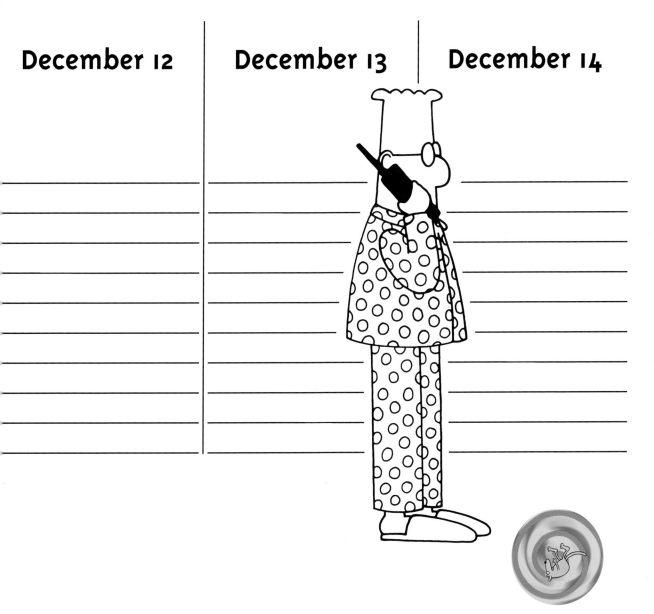

December 15

St Joseph

Call Hospital

12/16/

10:30 Focazio's
Office
973-777-7899 Broad St.
Sherry

11/16/04
1135 - Broad
ultra Sound
11:30 AM

December 16

Call Hospital for
xray

11/16
Ultra Sound
1135 Broad St
Anna
appointment 11:30
973 - 569 - 6300
St Joseph

Passaic B.L.   xray mammogram
973 - 365 - 4450

December 17

December 18

December 19

December 20

December 21	December 22	December 23

December 24	December 25	December 26

December 27

December 28

December 29

I HIRED RENOWNED PSYCHOLOGIST DOGBERT TO HELP US ACHIEVE PEAK PERFORMANCE IN TEAMWORK.

PEAK PERFORMANCE IS SOMEWHAT RELATIVE. YOU'RE A HIGHLY DYSFUNCTIONAL TEAM, SO WE MUST SET REALISTIC GOALS.

WHAT WOULD BE A REALISTIC GOAL FOR US?

I THINK I CAN POSTPONE CANNABILISM.

S. Adams   E-mail: SCOTTADAMS@AOL.COM   © 1995 United Feature Syndicate, Inc. (NYC)

December 30

December 31

Days I Don't Have To Show Up to Work.

January 1, New Year's Day

Third Monday in January, Martin Luther King. Jr's. Birthday

February 12, Lincoln's Birthday

February 14, Valentine's Day

Third Monday in February, President's Day

March 17, St. Patrick's Day

March or April, Easter Sunday

April 1, April Fool's Day

Second Sunday in May, Mother's Day

Last Monday in May, Memorial Day

Third Sunday in June, Father's Day

July 4, Independence Day

First Monday in September, Labor Day

Second Monday in October, Columbus Day

October 31, Halloween

November 11, Veteran's Day

Fourth Thursday in November, Thanksgiving

December 25, Christmas Day

Tasks To dump On Others

Good Reasons Not To Jump Out Windows

Things To Do During Meetings

Time Wasters